3.95

Supersta...

Violin *Level 1*

**Basic skills and
pieces for beginners**

Mary Cohen

Also available:

Superstart *Violin Level 1*
Accompaniments for piano and/or violin

Robert Spearing & Mary Cohen
ISBN 0 571 51711 0

© 1997 by Faber Music Ltd
First published in 1997 by Faber Music Ltd
3 Queen Square London WC1N 3AU
Illustrations by Todd O'Neill
Typesetting by Stephen Keeley
Cover design by S & M Tucker
Printed in England by Halstan & Co Ltd

ISBN 0 571 51319 0

FABER *ff* MUSIC

To the Pupil

Superstart Violin Level 1 is a book for you to explore with your teacher in lessons and to share with your family and friends. There are always lots of things to do (and show off) and there's real music to play as soon as you've learned to pick up your violin. If no-one at home can play the duet lines or accompaniments, ask your teacher to record some so you can enjoy proper performances while you practise. The tunes are the sort you'll want to play over and over again – the best way to become a really good violinist – and when your tired arms need a rest there are cartoons, jokes and funny songs to keep you interested. Get those brains and fingers working hard and have fun!

P.S. Always ask your teacher to explain again if there is something you don't understand.

To the Teacher / Parent

Superstart Violin Level 1 is an interactive book, offering a proper musical experience at each tiny step, with lots of activities and real pieces to perform from the very first lesson. The material is organised into progressive units which are either self-contained on one page or work as double spreads. Pages 3, 4 & 5 are for 'getting started' and pieces begin on page 6. The text is designed to be read to/with the pupil in a joint exploration of ideas, starting with the **bold** type face titles, then working through the musical text via the words and rhythms. The information in boxes is for discussion during lessons and also to help parents and pupils understand this week's objectives. There are four categories:

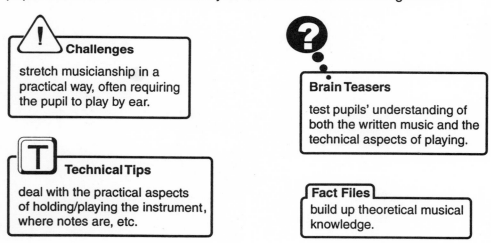

! Challenges stretch musicianship in a practical way, often requiring the pupil to play by ear.

? Brain Teasers test pupils' understanding of both the written music and the technical aspects of playing.

T Technical Tips deal with the practical aspects of holding/playing the instrument, where notes are, etc.

Fact Files build up theoretical musical knowledge.

The music in *Superstart Violin Level 1* uses the first finger pattern throughout and to aid theoretical understanding is written using rhythms which fit against a ♩ pulse. It is strongly recommended that some form of sung/spoken word scheme is used to establish good rhythm – the one introduced from page 12 onwards is a suggestion only and teachers should use another if they prefer.

Mary Cohen

Getting started...

First pit your wits against Professor Peg-Box and his gravity-defying violin

Match the names and numbers:

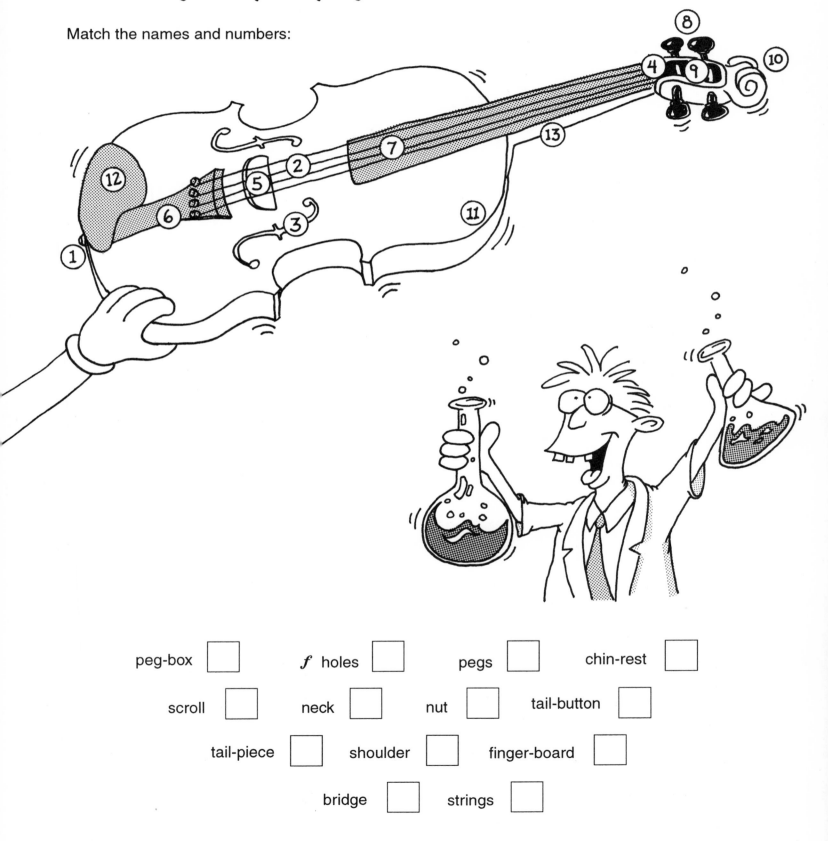

peg-box ☐   𝑓 holes ☐   pegs ☐   chin-rest ☐

scroll ☐   neck ☐   nut ☐   tail-button ☐

tail-piece ☐   shoulder ☐   finger-board ☐

bridge ☐   strings ☐

Now catch your gravity-defying* violin...

(Not to be taken too literally!)

Sing this song as you do the actions (check or complete the action during pauses)

Oh, Pick your vi- o- lin up, Float it through the sky...

Land it on your shoul- der, Keep the scroll up high.

T Technical Tip

Introducing the violin hold: Left-hand fingers should grasp the shoulder of the violin firmly, making the instrument easier to manoeuvre. Starting with your violin raised above shoulder level, try to slot it into a good, balanced position behind the back of the collar-bone. As the strings should be parallel to the ground, the scroll needs to be very slightly higher than the bridge. You could also use your right-hand index finger to check that the tail-button is exactly opposite the middle of the throat.

T Technical Tip

Move your hand off the shoulder of the violin to a relaxed position where the neck of the violin meets the shoulder – with your thumb to the left of the neck and all the fingers loose and able to move freely. "See-sawing", "strumming" and "wriggling" should help to keep your left arm relaxed. Before "tapping", check that you have short fingernails!

See-saw with your el - bow, Give your strings a strum...

Wrig - gle all your fin - gers, Tap tap on the drum

* The violin will feel light and gravity-defying
  if you keep 'thinking' a floating feeling into
  your left arm. (If your arm sinks, refloat it!)

Signor Pizzicato Proudly Presents...

Four Concertos for Open Strings
1. Asturias
(adapted from Albeniz)

Pluck the A string steadily in time with the violin duet part or piano accompaniment.

Pluck   the   A   Pluck   the   A   *etc.*

Keep playing until the accompaniment stops.
Listen out for three strong chords, then stop exactly with the fourth.
To make the piece harder you could play your part at twice the speed:

A string pizz – i – ca – to   A string pizz – i – ca – to   *etc.*

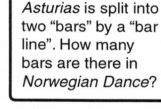

Challenge

Ask your teacher to record some of the duet lines for you so you can practise and perform at home.

Brain Teaser

Asturias is split into two "bars" by a "bar line". How many bars are there in *Norwegian Dance*?

2. Norwegian Dance No. 3
(adapted from Grieg)

Pluck   the   D   string,   Pluck   the   D   string   *etc.*

Pluck the D string steadily in time with the violin duet part or piano accompaniment.
As in the first piece, you need to keep playing your part until the accompaniment stops.
Listen out for a very low note.

To make the piece harder you could play your part at twice the speed:

Pizz – i – ca – to   on   the   D   string   *etc.*

3. Prelude to l'Arlésienne Suite

(adapted from Bizet)

Pluck the G string steadily in time with the violin duet part or piano accompaniment. The composer Bizet based this music on an old French tune called March of the Kings, so imagine you are playing for a very grand procession, long ago. Let your whole arm weight help you strum the string, leaving the sound to ring freely after each note.

Strum   Ring   Strum   Ring

etc. Listen out for two pizzicato chords at the end and stop with the third.

4. Raindrop Prelude

(adapted from Chopin)

The E string feels much more 'wirey' than the others and will break if tugged hard, so be careful and play this piece gently and quietly, using the soft pad of your finger. Whisper the word 'see'.

See   the   shin - y   rain - drops   drip - ping   *etc.*

Roll up, roll up for Major Marvel's
? # Musical Menagerie

> **Brain Teaser**
>
> Put a ring round all the names with 2 syllables, e.g. ADDER
>
> Put a box round all the names with 4 syllables, e.g. ALLIGATOR
>
> Put a squiggle round all the names with 1 syllable, e.g. ANT

armadillo   aardvark   (adder)   [alligator]   {ant}   beaver

badger   bison   bat   bed bug   bullfrog   camel

caterpillar   cat   cassowary   cheetah   cricket   cuckoo

donkey   duck   dolphin   dormouse   dog   eel   emu

fish   flea   fruit-fly   frog   goose   gerbil   giant panda

glow-worm   golden eagle   goat   goldfish   grass snake

> **⚠ Challenge 1**
>
> Fit all these creatures' names against a steady ♩ beat, which you can tap with your foot.

Now mix and match to make your own music

Pluck the name rhythms beginning with A on the A string.

Pluck the name rhythms beginning with D on the D string.

Pluck the name rhythms beginning with E on the E string.

Pluck the name rhythms beginning with G on the G string.

For example:

Arm – a – dill – o   Aard – vark   Dol – phin   Duck   *etc.*

> **⚠ Challenge 2**
>
> Ask your teacher to play the name rhythms beginning with B, C and F. Which open strings sound good played at the same time as B, C or F, and which ones clash?
>
> B sounds good with.......... F sounds good with..........
>
> C sounds good with.......... B clashes with..........
>
> F clashes with.......... C clashes with..........

Introducing the weightless bow...

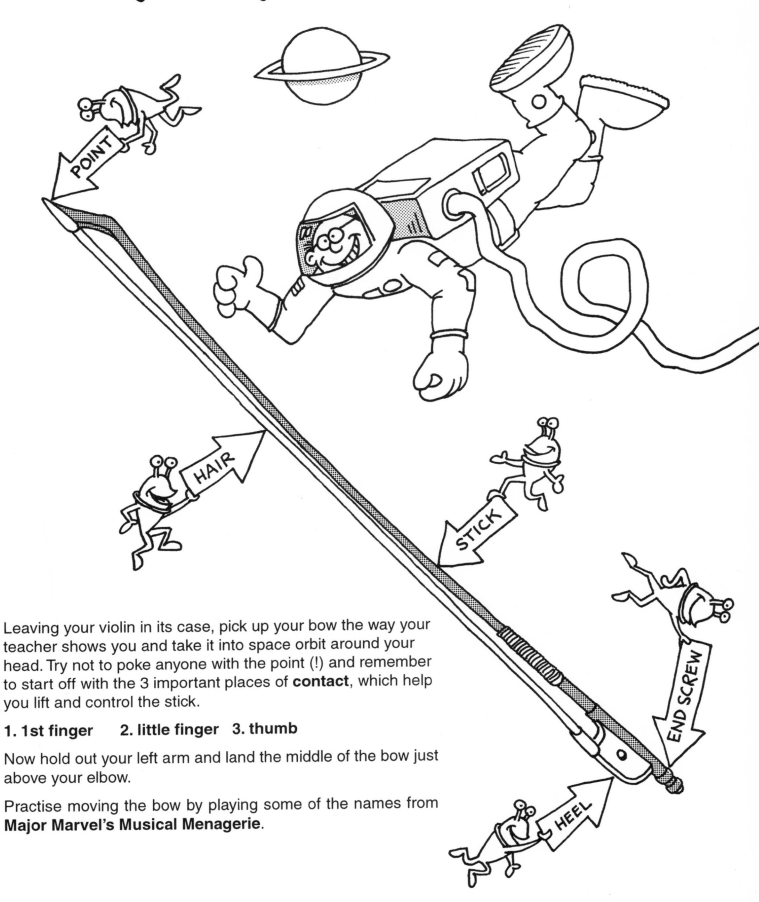

Leaving your violin in its case, pick up your bow the way your teacher shows you and take it into space orbit around your head. Try not to poke anyone with the point (!) and remember to start off with the 3 important places of **contact**, which help you lift and control the stick.

1. 1st finger   2. little finger   3. thumb

Now hold out your left arm and land the middle of the bow just above your elbow.

Practise moving the bow by playing some of the names from **Major Marvel's Musical Menagerie.**

Banana Swingboat Song

Try to imagine that your bow hand is swinging in a banana-shaped swingboat as you play the notes.

etc.

Stop playing when you hear the second cuckoo call in the teacher's part.

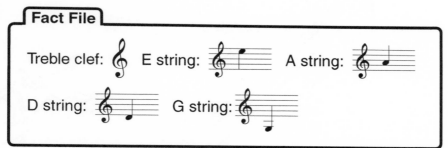

Fact File

Treble clef: E string: A string:

D string: G string:

Fill in the missing notes so you can play two more duet versions of the Banana Swingboat Song with your teacher. Which do you like best?

10

Banana Bubble Gum

'Draw' a huge bubble in the air with your arm each time you lift the bow off the string.

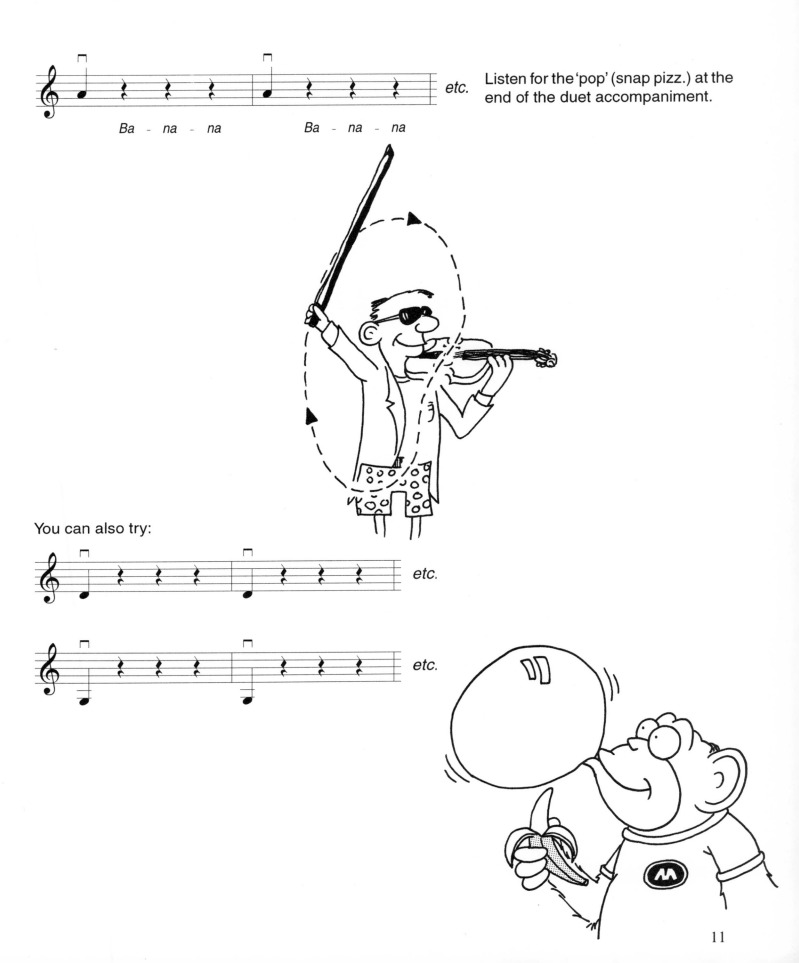

Ba - na - na   Ba - na - na

etc.

Listen for the 'pop' (snap pizz.) at the end of the duet accompaniment.

You can also try:

etc.

etc.

Name that Rhythm....

Using these rhythm names may help you to read new pieces more easily, and also suggest how much bow you need to use. See page 47 for a list of standard names.

Roll a Rhythm - Select a String!

Roll the dice to choose a rhythm…   …and again to select a string.

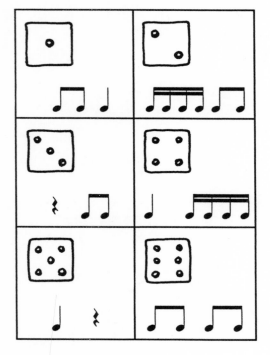

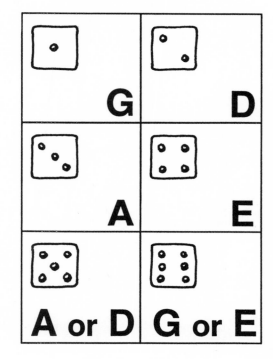

Play each rhythm you've rolled **four** times.

Professor Peg-Box spends an afternoon in the garden...

Copy Cat

Listen to the copy cat rhythm while you "wait wait".

wait   wait   co - py   cat

Copy Caterpillar

wait   wait   co - py   cat - er - pil - lar

loud whisper

co - py   cat - er - pil - lar

Fact File

│ Double bar line

The end of the piece

Caterpillar, Butterfly

Listen

Cat- er - pil - lar but-ter- fly

5

7

float bow off into space

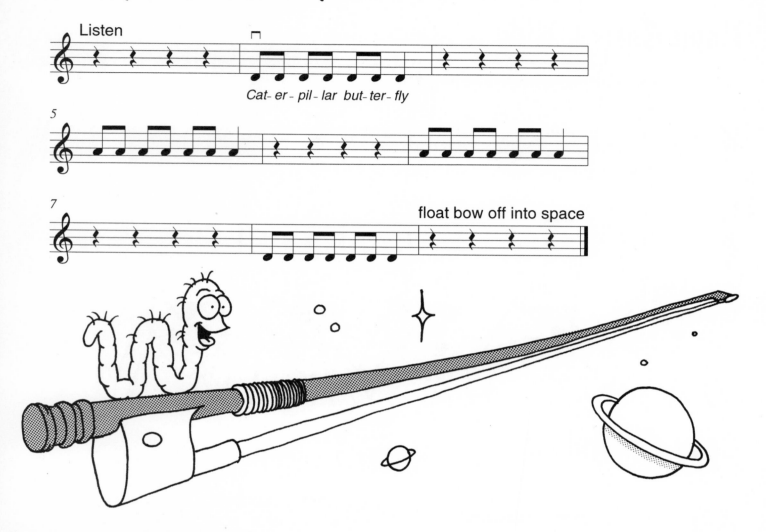

Butterfly, Flutter By

Listen

But - ter -fly,   flut -ter by

4

7

9

Mister Misterioso and his Amazing Magic Carpet Ride...

Before stepping aboard the magic carpet, you need to practise playing really long notes with your bow, going from the heel to the point and back several times. Your teacher will show you how to *glissando* with one finger at a time lightly up and down the strings.

To stop the glass of lemonade falling off the small magic carpet when you fly around with your *glissandos*, imagine your left hand is sliding very slightly down-hill when it moves towards your face, and very slightly up-hill when it moves towards the scroll.

Check with your teacher that you understand how to do the repeats and the Da Capo.

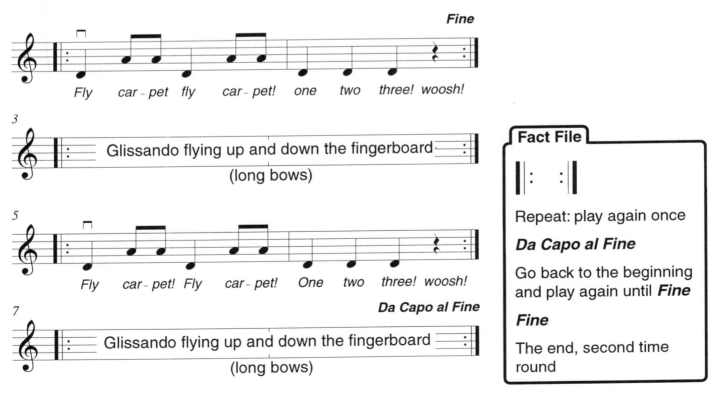

Fine

Fly car‑pet fly car‑pet! one two three! woosh!

3

Glissando flying up and down the fingerboard

(long bows)

5

Fly car‑pet! Fly car‑pet! One two three! woosh!

Da Capo al Fine

7

Glissando flying up and down the fingerboard

(long bows)

Fact File

|: :|

Repeat: play again once

Da Capo al Fine

Go back to the beginning and play again until *Fine*

Fine

The end, second time round

The Good Sound Guide

Sing as you play:

2. Too much rosin makes an itty gritty sound,
   Too much rosin makes an itty gritty sound,
   Too much rosin makes an itty gritty sound
   – so just go 'down, up, down'. *

   Flex your fingers etc.

3. If you skid you'll make an eaky squeaky sound,
   If you skid you'll make an eaky squeaky sound,
   If you skid you'll make an eaky squeaky sound,
   – so keep your bowing straight!

   Flex your fingers etc.

* 3 wipes of rosin

The Song of the Australian Bee Eater

Sing and play:

Maybe Abey Astronaut...

"earth" notes

"space" notes

May - be   Ab - ey   Ast - ro - naut   is   up   in   space...

May - be through a   te - le - scope I'd   see   his   face!

May - be   Ab - ey   Ast - ro - naut   is   look - ing   down...

May - be   Ab - ey   Ast - ro - naut   can   see   my   town!

Float bow into space
while you listen to the piano

Brain Teaser 1

Draw boxes round the "earth" notes
and squiggles round the "space" notes

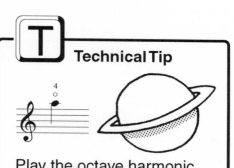

Technical Tip

Play the octave harmonic
half-way along the A string
with your little finger just
touching the string lightly,
(not pressing it down). This
note is called A.

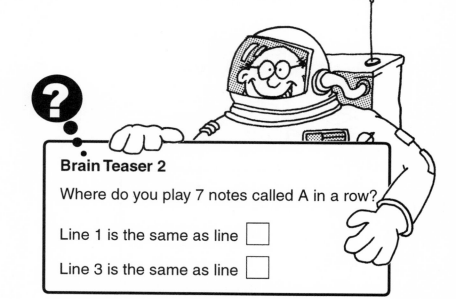

Brain Teaser 2

Where do you play 7 notes called A in a row?

Line 1 is the same as line ☐

Line 3 is the same as line ☐

Some more Maybes....

Maybe it would be fun to...   (page 6)
  go back and show Signor Pizzicato how three of his four concertos
  would sound played Arco (with the bow).
  Which one sounds best if you stick to playing it pizzicato?

Maybe you could...   (page 8)
  play the animal names beginning with **B** in Major Marvel's Musical
  Menagerie.

Maybe you could roll some longer rhythms   (page 12)
  and play them on **As** and **Bs**

Maybe the Amazing Magic Carpet Ride   (page 15)
  would sound good played on the A and E strings – ask your teacher
  to play the accompaniment one string higher too.

Maybe you could find out...
  what first fingers on the **G**, **D** & **E** strings sound like.

Maybe you could think of some maybes of your own!

  ....

  ....

  ....

  ....

Maybe you could give your brain a rest....

Hungry Penguins on Parade

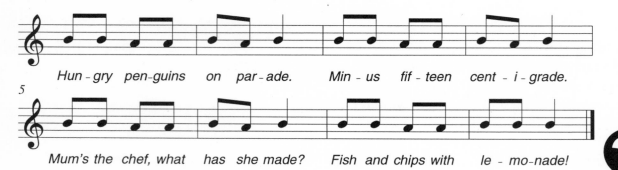

Hun - gry pen-guins on par - ade. Min - us fif - teen cent - i - grade.

Mum's the chef, what has she made? Fish and chips with le - mo-nade!

Recipe

Always prepare your musical ingredients carefully.

Adapt this recipe of ideas for every tune you learn with your teacher.

1. Sing the song with words

2. Work out the rhythm names and bow them in the air: short short short short short short long, etc.

3. Sing or say the finger numbers and open strings: one one **A A**, etc.

4. Sing or say the pitch names: **B B A A**, etc.

5. Play the tune.

6. When you can play the tune easily, ask your teacher to accompany you with one of the ostinatos.

7. Learn the ostinato parts and accompany your teacher.

Brain Teaser

Draw a ring round the first two bars.

Now find two more matching pairs of bars and draw rings round them.

Challenge

Vary the menu – try playing Hungry Penguins and the accompaniment one string higher.

Check with your teacher that you understand all the instructions, especially the words: bar, pitch, duet, accompaniment, rhythm, ostinato.

Ostinato duet accompaniments

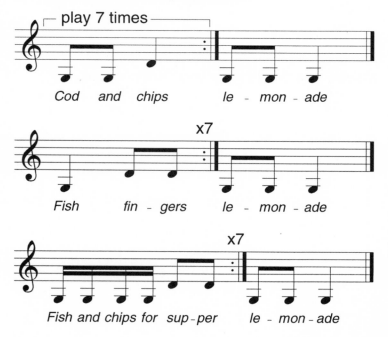

play 7 times

Cod and chips le - mon - ade

x7

Fish fin - gers le - mon - ade

x7

Fish and chips for sup - per le - mon - ade

More from the Menagerie

Little short and **Short little** have a competition with **Little tiny** to see who can think of the most creatures with the same rhythm as their own names

Fact File

♫ ♩   'Little short'

♫ ♩   'Short little'

♫   'Little tiny'

(All three fit against the same beat)

Little short   Short little   Little tiny

Brain Teaser

Draw rings round names with the same rhythm as **little short**, squiggles round names that match **short little**, and boxes round names that match **little tiny**.

stick insect   ant-eater   porcupine   oyster-catcher   nightingale   golden pheasant

mud skipper   antelope   praying mantis   howler monkey   pelican   ladybird

sea-urchin   rattlesnake   scorpion   caterpillar   bush-baby   salamander

harvest mouse   grasshopper   wood-pecker   water boatman   terrapin

kingfisher   kangaroo   centipede   wood-pigeon   elephant

Final Score:

Little short............
Short little.............
Little tiny..............

A Spooky House (Oooh! Who's that tapping at the window?)

You can learn both parts of this duet.
Prepare carefully – see the recipe on page 20.

tap   tap   tap

Technical Tip

Tap gently on the music stand with the screw end of your bow or gently bounce the wood of your bow against the string *(col legno)*.

D octave harmonic, found half-way along the D string (called D)

E octave harmonic, found half-way along the E string (called E)

Some skeletons, rattling around after midnight

You can learn both parts of this duet too.

Challenge

Make up some different rhythms for the skeletons

Gruesome Grub – the worst meal ever....

Prepare the ingredients for each piece carefully (remember the recipe on page 20).

Stir-Fried Centipedes

Brain Teaser 1

Draw a (ring) round bar 1 and any others like it.

Draw a [box] round bar 2 and any others like it.

Wriggly Worm Stew

Brain Teaser 2

Draw a [box] round bar 1 and any others like it.

Draw a (ring) round bar 2 and any others like it.

Draw a { squiggle } round bar 3 and any others like it.

Brain Teaser

Look out for any bars that match and draw boxes, rings or squiggles round them.

Caterpillar Dumplings

uurgh!

Nettle Pie with Chocolate Sauce

T **Technical Tip**

G octave harmonic, found half-way along the G string (called G)

Red Chilli Milkshake

Captain Fortissimo comes to the rescue with his fire engines...

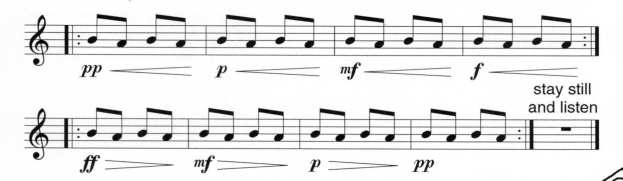

stay still and listen

Hot News! Number two joins the Captain's team...

One of the firemen has found some fragments of music. Play them and see if you recognise which well-known tunes they come from. Write the name of each tune below.

- - - - - - - - - - - - - - - - - -

- - - - - - - - - - - - - - - - - -

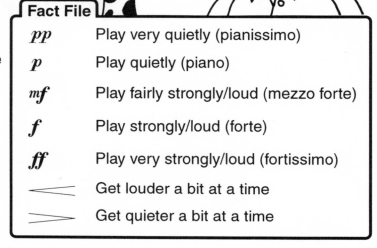

Fact File

pp	Play very quietly (pianissimo)
p	Play quietly (piano)
mf	Play fairly strongly/loud (mezzo forte)
f	Play strongly/loud (forte)
ff	Play very strongly/loud (fortissimo)
<	Get louder a bit at a time
>	Get quieter a bit at a time

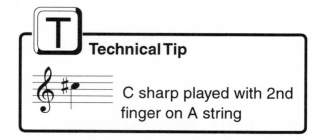

Technical Tip

C sharp played with 2nd finger on A string

- - - - - - - - - - - - - - - - - - - -

Using the same fingering, try playing these fragments on the **D**, **G** and **E** strings.

Faded Fragments

The firemen have found a few more fragments of music, but these have some very faded notes, which are hard to read. Look at them carefully and fill in the missing bits.

Technical Tip

F sharp played with 2nd finger on D string

G sharp played with 2nd finger on E string

B played with 2nd finger on G string

Percival's Secret Passion is...

You can play both parts of this duet but learn the top part first.

Per-ci-val's se-cret pas-sion is   Pep-per-mint choc'-late bars!

pizz.

He will eat them on the bus,   (Neat-ly and with-out a fuss),   Pep-per-mint choc'-late bars!

T Technical Tip

G played with 3rd finger on D string

D played with 3rd finger on A string

A played with 3rd finger on E string

This is the same music starting one string higher.

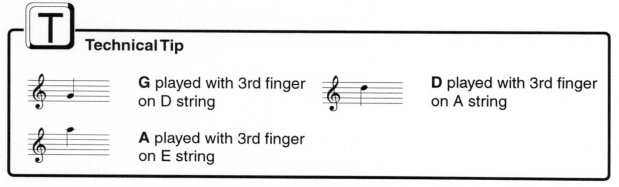

Per-ci-val's se-cret pas-sion is   Pep-per-mint choc'-late bars!

pizz.

He will eat them for his lunch,   a - ny time of day he'll munch   Pep-per-mint choc'-late bars!

Another version – what's happened to the duet line?

Per-ci-val's se-cret pas-sion is | Pep-per-mint choc'-late bars!

pizz.

If for tea you have him round, | bet-ter stock up half a pound, | Pep-per-mint choc'-late bars!

Technical Tip

C played with 3rd finger on G string

Scalebusters

You can now play all the notes of three scales going upwards (ascending).

A major scale (one octave)

D major scale (one octave)

G major scale (one octave)

Fact File 1

The music alphabet uses only the 7 letters ABCDEFG although you sometimes need to add words, e.g. 'sharp' after a letter name. If you play 8 notes going up or down in step, you will end with a note which has the same letter name as the one you started on. You will have played all the notes in one octave.

 Where sharp signs are needed, they have all been collected together next to the treble clef in a key signature.

Fact File 2

This kind of jump using notes with the same letter name is called playing the interval of an octave

29

Twinkle, Twinkle Little Bat

Wolfgang Amadeus Mozart and Lewis Carroll* discuss bats and
tea-trays in three different keys and three different moods…

Chirpy (like a bat)

Twin-kle, twin-kle lit-tle bat,   How I won-der what you're at…   Up a-bove the world you fly,

Like a tea-tray in the sky,   Twin-kle, twin-kle lit-tle bat,   How I won-der what you're at…

More thoughtful

Gloomy (like a tea-tray with spilt tea sloshing all over it…)

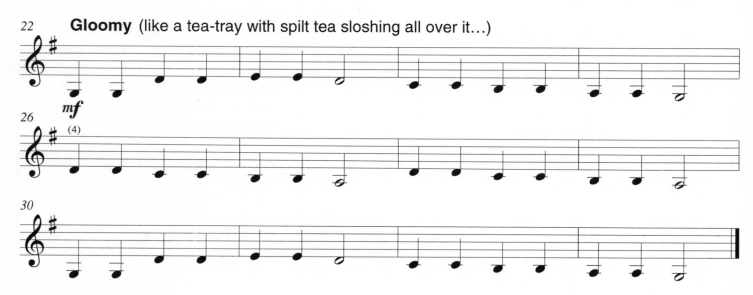

* Mozart wrote a set of variations on this French folk tune in
  1778, long before the English rhyme *Twinkle, twinkle* was
  written. Lewis Carroll's tea-tray version of the words appears
  in *Alice in Wonderland*.

Brain Teaser

Why is the stem of the
first note down not up?

! Challenge

Try your 4th finger on:

A string instead of open E.

D string instead of open A.

G string instead of open D.

Monsieur Arbeau's Sword Dance

(Thoinot Arbeau)

Key of A major:

Fine

(4)

Da Capo al Fine

⚠ Challenge

Remembering that it's a sword dance, choose a different tempo mark from the Fact File for each version. Your teacher will show you where to write it.

Key of D major:

Fine

(4)

Da Capo al Fine

Key of G major:

Fine

Da Capo al Fine

(4)   0

T Technical Tip

If you find it hard to play the notes with your 4th finger in tune, try relaxing and adjusting your left thumb.

Down on the Farm...
Old MacDonald had the Blues

p   *f*

1. Old Mac - Do - nald had the blues   E I E I O

p   *f*

All day he heard quacks and moos   E I E I O

p   *mp*   *mf*   *f*

Quacks and moos   Quacks and moos   All day long, rang the song of Quacks and moos

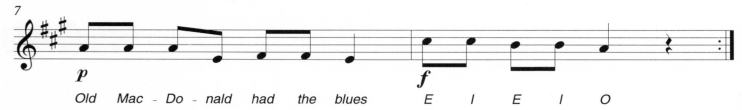

p   *f*

Old Mac - Do - nald had the blues   E I E I O

Coda (Verse 3)

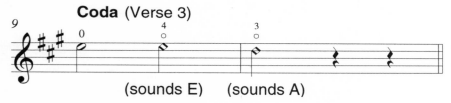

(sounds E)   (sounds A)

2. Old MacDonald moved to town – E I E I O
   He heard street noise all aroun' – E I E I O
   Honk honk HOOT
   Honk honk HOOT
   All day long, rang the song of
   Honk honk HOOT
   Old MacDonald had the blues – E I E I O

3. Old MacDonald had the blues – E I E I O
   From his hat down to his shoes – E I E I O
   Quacks and moos?
   Quacks and moos?
   Silly man – now he missed the quacks and
   moos....
   Old MacDonald had the blues – E I E I O

(There really is no pleasing some people!....)

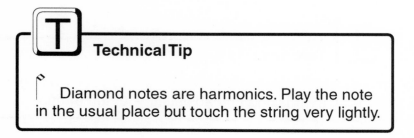

Technical Tip

Diamond notes are harmonics. Play the note in the usual place but touch the string very lightly.

Fact File	
Coda	Ending
>	Accent, play with more energy

Two very odd, old Farmers

VERSE 1

Allegro

Old Far-mer Buck he bought him a duck And he cut off her feet 'cos she walked in the muck. And

when she would-n't go for to roost like a crow. He cut off her head for to make her do so.

CHORUS

Andante

Why did he go and act this - a way?

Allegro

'Cos he were a fool, us all do say. 'Cos he were a fool, us all do say.

VERSE 2

Old Far-mer Bourn he bought him a horn For to rouse him-self up in the chill of the morn. He

al-ways do know when it's time for to blow. 'Cos he wakes up as soon as the roo - ster do crow!

REPEAT CHORUS

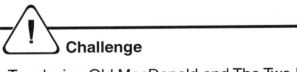

Challenge

Try playing Old MacDonald and The Two Farmers by ear on different strings, using the same fingering. There are only two other ways (not three) – why is that?

Postcards from Paris....

1. Brother Jack eats hot croissants by the light of the moon (Frère Jacques mange Croissants Chauds au Clair de la Lune)

Listen to the piano
for two bars

Start again with the piano
after one bar's rest

Brain Teaser

Draw a circle round the places where the key signature changes

2. We Can Can Can!

(Offenbach)

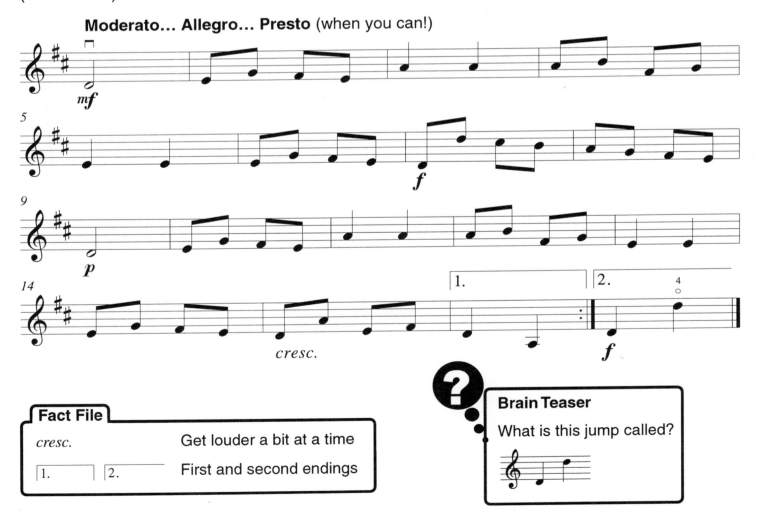

Postcards from America and Africa...

Go tell Aunt Nancy (the old grey goose is dead!)

Brain Teaser 1

Bar 1 makes a rhythmic sequence with bar 2.

Bar 5 makes a rhythmic sequence with bar 6 and bar…

Bar 9 makes a rhythmic sequence with bar…

Jikele Maweni

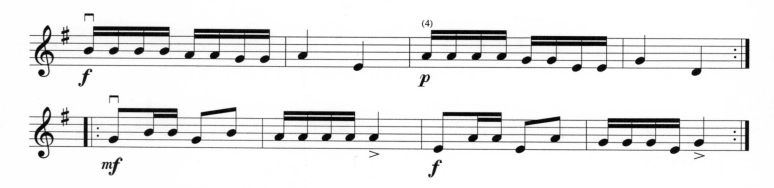

Brain Teaser 2

Bars 1 and 2 make a rhythmic sequence with bars......

Bars 5 and 6 make a rhythmic sequence with bars......

Don't Wanna!

"Hurry up and get out of bed!"

1. Don't wan-na get up yet.   Don't wan-na get up yet.

Don't wan-na get up yet, I   Don't wan-na get up yet!

"Make sure you wash properly!"

2. Don't wan-na wash be - hind my ears.   Don't wan-na wash be - hind my ears.

Don't wan-na wash be - hind my ears, I   Don't wan-na get up yet!

"If you don't get a move on you'll miss breakfast!"

3. Don't wan-na eat a - ny ce - re - al.   Don't wan-na eat a - ny ce - re - al.

Don't wan-na eat a - ny ce - re - al, I   Don't wan-na get up yet!

"I give up.... have you forgotten it's the school holidays and we're going out for the day?"

Brain Teaser

Here's the final verse. Does it need the same music as verse 1, 2 or 3?

Why did you let me stay in bed?
Why did you let me stay in bed?
Why did you let me stay in bed - I
Don't wanna miss the fun!

As you've noticed before – you just can't win with some people....

37

Scalebusters 2

You can now play one octave scales going down (descending) as well as going up (ascending).

A major scale

Ascending:

Descending:

They are often played with a special rhythm which makes them sound more like a tune.

Tune version:

D major scale

Ascending:

Descending:

! Challenge

Try the scales of D major and G major in tune versions

G major scale

Ascending:

Descending:

Have you noticed that the pattern you make with your open string and fingers for the first 4 notes of a scale is the same as the pattern for notes 5 - 8? These groups of 4 notes are called **tetrachords**.

So that's what a tetrachord is!

Brain Teasers

Circle the first tetrachord in the scale of A major.
Now look for the tetrachord in the scale of D major which uses exactly the same notes.

Circle the first tetrachord in the scale of D major.
Now look for the tetrachord in the scale of G major which uses exactly the same notes.

More Finger Skills

You can also play arpeggios (broken up chords) in the same keys as the scales on page 38.

in the same keys as the scales on page 38.

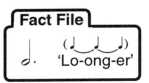

Fact File

'Lo-ong-er'

A major arpeggio

Ascending: Descending: Tune version:

D major argeggio

Ascending: Descending:

⚠ Challenge

Try the arpeggios of D major and G major in tune versions

G major arpeggio

Ascending: Descending:

Keep on track!

Roll the dice to see which map route to follow.

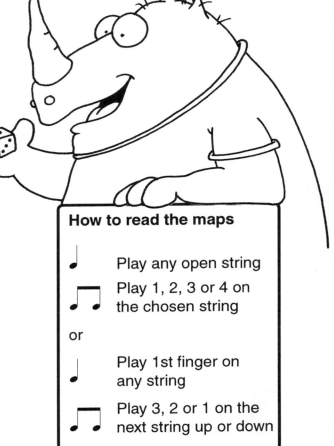

How to read the maps

♩   Play any open string

🎵   Play 1, 2, 3 or 4 on the chosen string

or

♩   Play 1st finger on any string

🎵   Play 3, 2 or 1 on the next string up or down

The aim of this game is to play clear sounding notes with strong independent fingers.

39

Oliver Cromwell lay buried and dead

Oliver Cromwell lay buried and dead.
Hee-haw, buried and dead.
There grew an old apple tree over his head.
Hee-haw, over his head.

Apples were rip'ning and ready to fall,
Hee-haw, ready to fall.
There came an old woman to gather them all,
Hee-haw, gather them all.

Oliver rose and he gave her a drop,
Hee-haw, gave her a drop.
Which made the old woman go hipperty hop,
Hee-haw, hipperty hop.

T   **Technical Tip**

V V   Two bows in the
same direction

Brain Teaser

Draw a box round the note which fits the words in the boxes

Just for a change... A happy person!

I had a cat and the cat pleased me.
I fed my cat by yonder tree.
Cat goes fiddle-dee-dee!

I had a hen and the hen pleased me.
I fed my hen by yonder tree.
Hen goes chimmy chuck, chimmy chuck,
Cat goes fiddle-dee-dee!

I had a dog and the dog pleased me.
I fed my dog by yonder tree.
Dog goes woof woof, woof woof,
Hen goes chimmy chuck, chimmy chuck,
Cat goes fiddle-dee-dee!

Brain Teasers

There are 4 beats in most bars of this piece. But how many beats are there in the "Hen goes" bar?
The note with a ring round it is called an upbeat. Find the upbeat in the pieces on pages 36 and 40.

Fact File

♪ 'Short'

♩. ♪ (♩ ♪ ♪) 'Long add short'

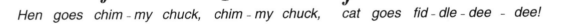

 Challenge

Can you add extra verses with appropriate animal noises?

Merrily we Roller Blade

Allegretto

Verse 1

Verse 2

Verse 3

1. *Merrily we roller blade, roller blade, roller blade,*
   Merrily we roller blade, trying not to knock too many people over!

2. *Merrily we roller blade, roller blade, roller blade,*
   Merrily we roller blade, trying not to crash into too many walls.

3. *Merrily we roller blade, roller blade, roller blade,*
   Merrily we roller blade, trying not to...

> **Fact File**
>
> ⌒ ‿ Slurs – keep the bow moving smoothly in the same direction for two or more notes, without making a gap in the sound.

> ⚠ **Challenge 1**
>
> Can you make up your own ending for verse 3, words and music?
>
> **Challenge 2**
>
> Try playing this tune by ear at a slower speed in the key of D major.

> **Brain Teaser**
>
> The *Allegretto* version is in the key of A major.
>
> Which key is The Happy Hippos in?

The Happy Hippos go Skating

Adagio

From the depths of the sea to the middle of a wood...

If you meet an Octopus,
You'd better shake hands carefully...

Fact File

𝄾 Short rest (wait)

T **Technical Tip**

Two octave harmonic on the **D** string – touch 3rd finger lightly where you normally play the note **G**. This note is called **D**.

The sound is two octaves higher than open D.

Reminder: an 8-note jump between two notes of the same letter name is called one octave.

Cuckoo Echoes

Fact File

Extra sharps (e.g. bar 9) which are not in the key signature are called accidentals

43

More Musical Postcards – from France and Germany...

Whence is that Goodly Fragrance?

Brain Teaser 1

Most bars in this piece need two bows. Can you find three bars where you use only one bow?

Fact File

3/4 Three ♩ ('long') beats in a bar.

2/4 Two ♩ ('long') beats in a bar.

These numbers are called time signatures.

Ho-La-Hi

Brain Teaser 2

How many pieces can you find in 3/4 and 2/4 earlier in the book?

Write the 3/4 or 2/4 time signature at the beginning of each one.

... and from Scotland, Ireland and America

Queen Mary

Fact File

♪ A very quick upbeat

4/4 Four ♩ beats in a bar

Michael Finnegan

There was an old man called Mi – chael Fin-ne–gan, He grew whis – kers on his chin – ne–gan, The
wind came up and blew them in a–gain, Poor old Mi – chael Fin–ne–gan, be– gin a–gain!

Someone's in the Kitchen with Dinah!

Da Capo al Fine

A final postcard from America...

Turkey in the Straw

With a swing!

... with a message on the back

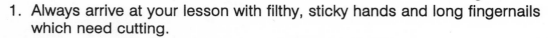

Seven useful tips

(to make you one of the worst pupils in the world)

1. Always arrive at your lesson with filthy, sticky hands and long fingernails which need cutting.

2. Forget to put your bow/violin in your case after practising, so you have a good chance of leaving one of them at home.

3. Leave all the pieces you are working at on your music-stand after practising so even if you remember your violin/bow, you will probably forget to bring your music.

4. Lose your practice notebook the second you arrive home – so you don't have to read it and you can aim for the world record of the pupil who has the most notebooks with only one page of writing.

5. Never ever look in your practice book (if you're being kind to trees and haven't lost it yet) to remind you what it is that you are supposed to be working at this week.

6. Always play pieces with as many of the mistakes you made first time round as possible, and definitely don't try to remember what it was you worked on in your lesson which solved this week's problems.

7. Don't practise until the day before your next lesson and if possible make sure you've left either your violin, bow or music with your teacher.

Have you any other great tips to pass on?

Fact File Update

Notes learned so far

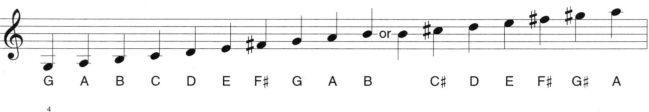

G   A   B   C   D   E   F♯   G   A   B   C♯   D   E   F♯   G♯   A

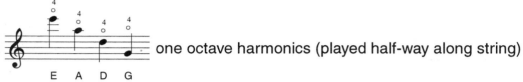 one octave harmonics (played half-way along string)

E   A   D   G

Rhythm names and standard names (English and American)

♩   'Long': crotchet (or quarter note)

♪   'Short': quaver (or eighth note)

♬   Semiquaver (or sixteenth note)

♫   'Short short': 2 quavers (or eighth notes)

𝄽   'Wait': crotchet rest (or quarter note rest)

   'Little tiny': 4 semiquavers (or sixteenth notes)

𝅗𝅥   'Long-er': minim (or half note)

𝅗𝅥.   'Lo-ong-er': dotted minim (or dotted half note)

   'Little short': 2 semiquavers + 1 quaver (or 2 sixteenth notes + 1 eighth note)

   'Short little': 1 quaver + 2 semiquavers (or 1 eighth note + 2 sixteenth notes)

♩. ♪   'Long add short': 1 dotted crotchet + 1 quaver (or 1 dotted quarter note + 1 eighth note)

Dynamics

f   Loud (forte)

p   Quiet (piano)

pp   Very quiet (pianissimo)

mf   Fairly strong/loud (mezzo forte)

ff   Very strong/loud (fortissimo)

◁   Get louder, a bit at a time

▷   Get quieter, a bit at a time

cresc.   Get louder, a bit at a time

Tempo

The speed at which you play a piece

Allegro   Fast and lively

Allegretto   Quite fast and lively

Andante   Slow walking speed

Adagio   Slow

Presto   Very fast

Moderato   Between fast and slow

Largo   Slow and dignified

Fact File Update continued...

Violin Technique

⊓   Down bow

V   Up bow

col legno   Bounce the wood of the bow gently against the string

        Diamond harmonics – touch string lightly instead of pressing

>   Play with more energy (accent)

⌒ ⌣   Slurs

Music Theory

      Treble clef

♯   Sharp

Key signatures :

G major   D major   A major

An accidental is an extra sharp,
not in the key signature

Time signatures:

$\frac{2}{4}$ $\frac{3}{4}$ $\frac{4}{4}$

2, 3 or 4 crotchet (quarter note) beats in a bar

| Bar-line

‖   Double bar-line

‖: :‖   Repeat signs

⌒   Pause

Da Capo al Fine
Go back to the beginning
and play again until **Fine**.

Fine   The end, last time round

Coda   Ending